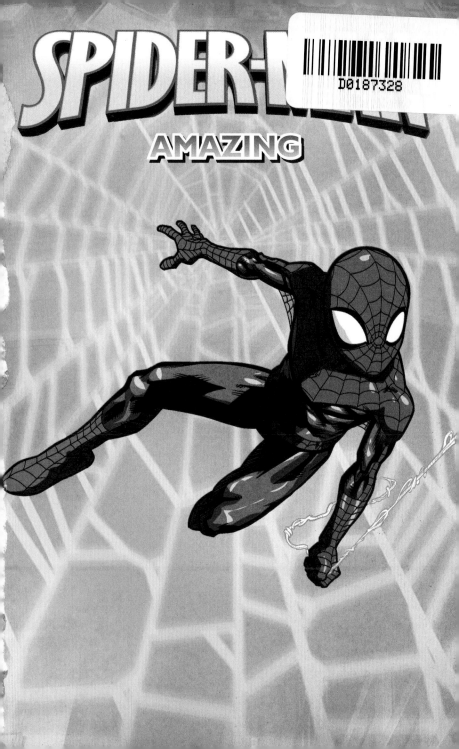

R-MAN

AMAZING

Writer: **Paul Tobin**

Penciler: **Matteo Lolli**

Inkers: **Christian Dalla Vecchia, Terry Pallot, Scott Koblish & Andrew Hennessy**

Colors: **Sotocolor**

Letters: **Dave Sharpe**

Cover Artists: **Karl Kerschl, Serge LaPointe & Nadine Thomas**

Assistant Editor: **Michael Horwitz**

Editor: **Nathan Cosby**

Marvel Age Spider-Man #1

Plot: **Stan Lee & Steve Ditko**

Script: **Daniel Quantz**

Pencilers: **Mark Brooks & Jonboy Meyers**

Inkers: **Mark Brooks & Pat Davidson**

Colors: **Danimation with Simon Yeung & Udon's Larry Molinar**

Letters: **Virtual Calligraphy's Randy Gentile**

Cover Artist: **Mark Brooks**

Assistant Editors: **Mackenzie Cadenhead & Nick Lowe**

Editor: **C.B. Cebulski**

Consulting Editor: **Ralph Macchio**

Collection Editor: **Cory Levine**

Editorial Assistants: **James Emmett & Joe Hochstein**

Assistant Editor: **Alex Starbuck** • Associate Editor: **John Denning**

Editors, Special Projects: **Jennifer Grünwald & Mark D. Beazley**

Senior Editor, Special Projects: **Jeff Youngquist** • Senior Vice President of Sales: **David Gabriel**

Editor in Chief: **Joe Quesada** • Publisher: **Dan Buckley** • Executive Producer: **Alan Fine**

#1

Twenty blocks away.

Project is going... strange.

I wanted to do this on Spider-Man because he's so bizarre.

But the more I do these interviews, the more ALL New Yorkers seem weird. It makes Spider-Man seem less foreign. Not as scary.

Not sure how I feel about that.

--AND THEN SOMETIMES I *DREAM* I'M SPIDER-MAN. IN *SPACE*. LIKE WITH *LASERS*.

YOU EVER HAVE THOSE DREAMS?

I GUESS SO

What makes Spider-Man different? That's the question. These people I'm talking to...could they do what Spider-Man does?

I don't mean climb walls or swing around on webs. I mean have the courage to risk it all for what's right.

That's IF Spider-Man is doing the right thing. Still not sure about that. It's impossible enough to tell what normal people are really thinking...

...let alone what's going on beneath that red mask.

SPIDER-MAN? WELL, I'D HAVE TO SAY HE'S *FASCINATING*. *SURE* WOULD LIKE TO *MEET* HIM.

AND ARE YOU A *NATIVE* NEW YORKER, SIR?

LESTER. THE NAME'S *LESTER*. AND I'M JUST IN TOWN FOR *BUSINESS*.

WOW! GOOD SHOT!

YEAH.

I *NEVER* MISS.

#2

AWPP!

SKRRR

HEY!

RAFF
RAFF
RAFF
RARRR

WHAT'S
GOING--

UNHHH!

WMMWWWHUMMMMM

Twenty minutes later.

WHERE ARE YOU?

HIDING IN THE BUSHES OVER BY THE PRETZEL CART. I CAN SEE *YOU*.

I'M WAVING MY HAND.

PETER? WHEN YOU SAID YOU WERE *HIDING* I THOUGHT YOU WERE BEING *SPIDER-MAN*.

WHY IS *PETER PARKER* HIDING?

UMMM...BECAUSE I JUST GET *USED* TO IT, I GUESS.

ALSO, THIS DOG IS *STOLEN*.

WHAT *HAPPENED*?

IT WAS A *DOGNAPPING*. SOME GUYS ON *MOTOR SCOOTERS*.

MOTOR SCOOTERS? *THAT'S* NOT VERY...*AWE-INSPIRING*.

#3

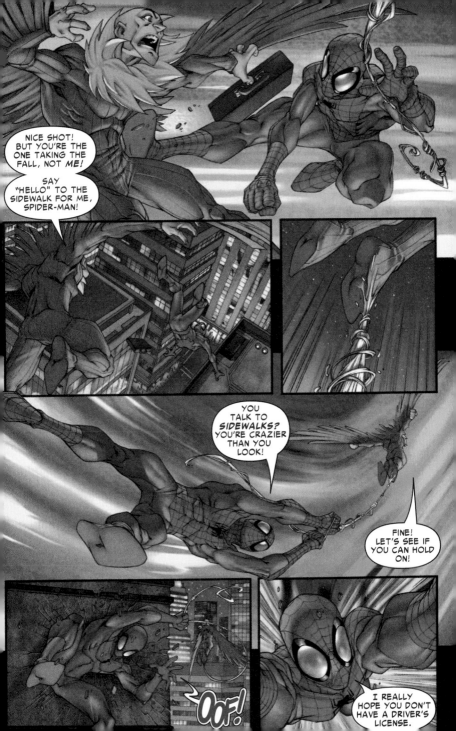

End.